May 2021,

Find your adventi

&

Follow your dreams!

Sandra
Marichal

The Round the World Wanderer

Inspired by a true story

The Round the World Wanderer

Published by Marichal-Ragot Publishing 2020

Editing & Proofreading: Nicky Miller
Illustration & Cover: Fanny Ozda
Layout Design: Bastien Marichal
Photography: Maéva Bardy

ISBN: 978-1-5272-6190-7

For **every** child

Hey kid! This is Sandra.
I am writing this letter from
our sailing yacht which has
just crossed the equator.
I am on an adventure to
sail beyond the horizon
and find what
is out there

Tonight, the moon is so bright it feels like someone has forgotten to turn the light off.

The sky is so clear that we can steer the boat using only the stars.

I can see people asleep on deck without my torch.

My crew is tired, you see.

We've been sailing for seven months.

We left London and sailed south, braving huge waves crossing the Atlantic Ocean, to visit a very friendly country called Uruguay. We even chased Hurricane Lorenzo on the way.

Then we sailed all
the way back across the
Atlantic Ocean to Cape Town,
the most southern city in Africa.

We were battered by enormous storms on the way. The waves were taller than houses and crashed over the boat covering everywhere and everyone with water.

Being on deck was dangerous and we had to be very careful not to fall overboard, so we clipped our lifejackets to the boat to keep us safe.

We then sailed towards the South Pole. The air was so cold and so wet that it felt like it was raining even inside the boat! The water was everywhere and everything was damp, all the time.

The only dry place was inside our warm, cosy sleeping bags.

When they swam too close to us, we had to be careful not to bump into them, not to hurt them. If they hit us and made a hole in the boat, we might sink to the bottom of the sea.

We carried on sailing east. Around Australia, the bush fires were so fierce that the sky turned dark orange, even though we were many miles out at sea.

We sailed through the Great Barrier Reef and across the Coral Sea. We saw Papua New Guinea and many other mysterious islands right in the middle of the ocean.

Now we're heading north again to the South China Sea, together with a fleet of boats who are going in the same direction. We've been sailing for weeks without stopping. We take turns to sleep and eat, swapping places every few hours, sailing on and on.

It's a very long time on a boat, and it's really hot now, especially without a proper shower. So when we get too stinky, or too itchy, we get a black rubber bucket, fetch water from the ocean and pour it over ourselves. Fully dressed and always wearing our lifejackets to stay safe!

Today I had one of these
showers because I woke up from
my afternoon nap all sweaty.
I don't smell anymore. Phew!

We eat porridge every day for breakfast with bread and spread. I like marmalade but some crew eat a weird mix of peanut butter and marmite. Yuk!

My crewmates are always very hungry and eat a lot every day! Sometimes I bake muffins for them.

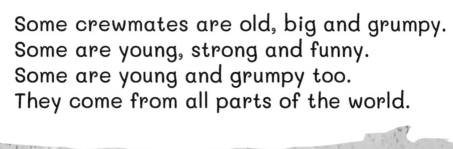

Some crewmates are old, big and grumpy.
Some are young, strong and funny.
Some are young and grumpy too.
They come from all parts of the world.

There's Manurere, the Māori sailor. She's strong and flexible but doesn't break, like the bamboo. She's quiet and stays silent most of the time. She can hoist a sail on her own and steer with her eyes closed. I think she has the spirit of the ancestral Pacific warriors inside her.

There's Mike who has already sailed all around the world, in the windiest and most dangerous places. He lost most of his hair there. He always smiles, knows a thousand jokes and drinks at least five milky teas a day. He spends hours solving cryptic crosswords! He's the nicest mate onboard.

There's also Holly who loves sewing. She goes around the boat with a needle in her hair, ready to stitch the sails back together when they get damaged by the storms. Once she sewed for three whole days and nights. It was so rough she wore a helmet because the boat was going up and down so much she could have banged her head against the ceiling.

There's Aser, the sailor from the cold north. She's got white skin and white short hair and she is very tall. She is the bow woman, always at the front of the boat, hoisting and dropping the very heavy and large headsails. She is fierce and always excited about getting wet in the big waves.

And there's Ian, the captain. He is the youngest but the scariest of all. He spends most of his time at the stern, right at the back of the boat, steering or looking at the sky to find wind. He decides where we go and when we change sails. He always stays calm and whispers his commands to the crew. He can also speak to birds.

We also see boobies, petrels and swallows. Some of them land right at the top of the mast when they need to rest.

I wish I could rest too, but we still have a long way to go. We discovered that there was land far beyond the horizon and that the world was round. We're now on the other side, so we must keep sailing to get back home.

COME SAIL WITH ME!

Colour the Clipper 70 boat hull and sails

Ask your parents to send me a picture of your
drawing at theroundtheworlder@gmail.com or
post it on Facebook or Instagram and
tag @roundtheworlder

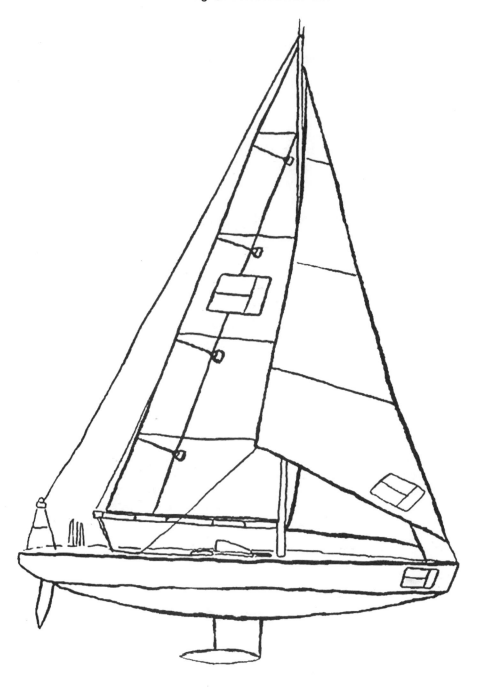

ACKNOWLEDGEMENTS

Thanks to Sir Robin Knox-Johnston and to the Clipper Round the World Yacht Race for the opportunity to sail around the world and for the support in sharing this incredible race with kids.

Thanks to Unicef UK for their partnership and for doing what you do. Hope this book helps.

Thanks to Fanny Ozda who embarked on this adventure not knowing where we were going or how we'd get there — she'd make a great sailor. Funnily, we never met in person.

Thanks to my brother Bastien Marichal for turning into a full publishing house design studio — he's done the book template, layout and file preparation. He's the real genius of the family.

Thanks to Nicky Miller for the editing, proofreading and being endlessly encouraging.

Thanks to Ian Wiggin, Mike Miller, Juscinta Grace, Aser Serigstad and Holly for agreeing to be featured in this book, you are every child's favourite characters! Thanks to the CV31 Race Crew and Race Crew Supporters, I will miss you all... except Charles, I hope I never see you again. And thanks to 'Colin from Accounts' for keeping us 'sane' in the middle of the ocean.

Thanks to the Sea Rescue Durban NSRI Station 05 for welcoming us and for facilitating the rescue of our crew members. And a massive thanks to Rob and Dee Stewart for their generosity (and mushrooms).

Thanks to Alex Cass for going through the thousand versions of this book, for coping with my moaning, grunting and hair-pulling moments and for gracefully accepting the rejection of most of his feedback.

Thanks to Andrea Edwards & Manouchka Elefant for guiding me through this complex (self-) publishing process.

Thanks to Romulo de Freitas and Roberto Vilchis for the help with font & graphics #FutureBranderForever

Thanks to the Sunday 6pm Book Club for talking about everything but books.

A very special thanks to my Mom Domie and my Dad Eric Marichal for the relentless support and hourly race tracker check-ins; for learning English to be able to speak with the other supporters; for travelling to the other side of the world to bring me merino undies, clean the bilges and service the winches; for picking up the phone in the middle of the night to calm me down as I tell you I broke yet another bone and I'm stuck in the middle of the ocean, crying. Thank you for making me believe anything was possible and for letting me go do it. I love you.

ABOUT THE AUTHOR

Sandra spent the last ten years working in Tech, Consulting and Finance, across Europe and Asia Pacific, before deciding to quit it all and start sailing around the world.

She's a Round the Worlder in the Clipper 2019-20 Round the World Yacht Race onboard Unicef. She is also the Team Coordinator - the crew manager: setting up the boat systems, job rotas, crew schedules and managing the boat relationship with the Race Office and outside world - all with the objective to improve the boat's overall racing performance.

Born French, she's visited over 65 countries and has thousands of travel anecdotes to tell. She's been to Antarctica - twice - once with Robert Swan OBE and then as a UN Women Ambassador. Sandra is also an engaged activist, raising awareness about the environmental impact of aircon systems in Singapore. She founded the #up2degrees movement and successfully lobbied the government to change public spaces regulations.

She's also a founding partner of Her Planet Earth - focusing on empowering women to fight climate change, and if she had one wish it would be to see more women going on adventures and protect the environment we thrive in. She hasn't got a home, she's a travelling nomad who lives out of her suitcase.

To discover more about Sandra's adventures, visit:

⚓ www.sandramarichalofficial.com
🅕 @sandramarichalofficial
🅞 @sandramarichalofficial

ABOUT THE ILLUSTRATOR

Fanny Ozda is a French illustrator based in Singapore. Ex-lawyer turned artist, she is the cartoonist for Le Petit Journal Singapore Edition and the co-founder of « Sketching Sundays Singapore », a community of artists meeting weekly to share ideas and advice on their latest art projects.

Fanny is a travel aficionada. She gets especially inspired by the beautiful countries of South-East Asia. She loves crochet, origami and all DIY arts & crafts. She even hand-stitches her own sketchbooks. She is a big fan of graphic novels which she collects despite her otherwise very minimalistic lifestyle.

She is a daydreamer, deeply connected to her inner-child, who sees the magic in the everyday life.